# PAUL

© PAUL FELL

## FROM THE PAGES OF
## HUSKERS ILLUSTRATED MAGAZINE

ISBN 0-934904-63-4
ISBN 978-0-934904-63-6

MANUFACTURED IN UNiTED STATES OF AMERiCA

J&L LEE CO.
P.O. BOX 5575
LiNCOLN, NE 68505
PRINTED BY SERVICE PRESS, HENDERSON, NE 68371

# HUSKERNUTZ

YOU AND YOUR PALS HAVE BEEN TO EVERY HUSKER
HOME GAME SINCE 1970 AND HAVE YET TO SET FOOT
IN MEMORIAL STADIUM.

# HUSKERNUTZ

YOUR WILL SPECIFIES THAT YOUR ASHES SHOULD BE SCATTERED OVER MEMORIAL STADIUM ON A HUSKER GAME DAY.

# HUSKERNUTZ

THE BOWL GAMES COME TO AN END FOR ANOTHER
YEAR AND LIFE BEGINS TO RETURN TO A MORE
NORMAL PACE IN HUSKER NATION.

# HUSKERNUTZ

YOU KEEP YOUR MONEY BURIED IN THE BACK YARD.
YOU KEEP YOUR HUSKER SEASON TICKETS IN A BANK
VAULT UNDER HEAVY SECURITY.

# HUSKERNUTZ

YOU'VE ALWAYS BELIEVED THAT IT PAYS TO DO
BUSINESS WITH YOUR HOMETOWN BANK.

# HUSKERNUTZ

YOU AND YOUR BEST BUDDY TRY TO MAKE IT TO AT LEAST ONE HUSKER GAME EACH SEASON.

# HUSKERNUTZ

IF YOU ARE COUNTING THE DAYS UNTIL THE END OF
SUMMER AND THE START OF FALL CAMP, THEN
YOU'RE A SERIOUS HUSKERNUT.

# HUSKERNUTZ

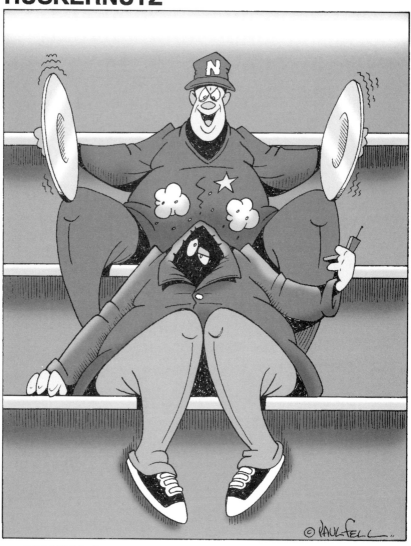

TALKING ON YOUR CELL PHONE COULD POSSIBLY
ANNOY SOME OF YOUR FELLOW FANS DURING
HUSKER GAMES.

# HUSKERNUTZ

SHOPPING FOR CHRISTMAS PRESENTS FOR YOUR
HUSKERNUT IS A NO-BRAINER.

# HUSKERNUTZ

YOU HAVE TO CHOOSE BETWEEN ATTENDING YOUR
WIFE'S GARDEN CLUB RECEPTION OR THE HUSKER
HOME OPENER.

# HUSKERNUTZ

YOU'RE NOT CRAZY ABOUT THOSE 11a.m. KICKOFF
TIMES FOR TELEVISION, BUT YOU COPE.

# HUSKERNUTZ

IT TAKES YOU LONGER TO GET READY ON GAME DAY
THAN IT DID FOR YOUR BRIDE TO PREPARE FOR THE
WEDDING.

# HUSKERNUTZ

**PEOPLE COME TO THOSE HOT, EARLY-SEASON HUSKER GAMES IN SOME AMAZING GETUPS.**

# HUSKERNUTZ

OTIS AND NELDA LOVE TO GET ALL GUSSIED UP FOR
HUSKER GAME DAYS.

# HUSKERNUTZ

YOU'VE NEVER BEEN ONE TO LET MINOR HEALTH
ISSUES STAND IN THE WAY OF BEING AT A HUSKER
HOME GAME.

# HUSKERNUTZ

WHEN YOUR GIRLFRIEND CHOSE CANDY AND
FLOWERS OVER TWO BASKETBALL TICKETS, YOU
KNEW THE RELATIONSHIP WAS DOOMED TO FAILURE.

# HUSKERNUTZ

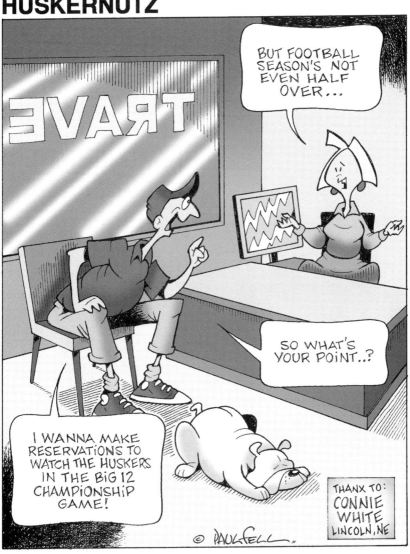

YOU ALWAYS ASSUME THE HUSKERS WILL BE PLAYING FOR THE CONFERENCE CHAMPIONSHIP IN DECEMBER.

# HUSKERNUTZ

YOUR WIFE ASKS IF YOU WANT TO GO WITH HER TO
THE POST-THANKSGIVING SALES.
YOU HAD NO IDEA THERE WAS SUCH A THING.

# HUSKERNUTZ

YOU EVENTUALLY GET TO THE AGE WHERE IT IS IMPOSSIBLE TO WATCH AN ENTIRE GAME THAT KICKS OFF LATER THAN 6 PM.

# HUSKERNUTZ

HOWIE AND LAVINIA GEAR UP FOR ANOTHER BIG
HUSKER BASEBALL SEASON.

# HUSKERNUTZ

YOU HAVE TO GET TO YOUR STADIUM SEAT WELL
BEFORE KICKOFF TO DEFEND AGAINST THOSE
DREADED "SPACE INVADERS".

# HUSKERNUTZ

# HUSKERNUTZ

A LITTLE WEATHER IS NO EXCUSE TO CANCEL A
PERFECTLY GOOD TAILGATE PARTY.

# HUSKERNUTZ

NOW WE ENTER THAT LONG DARK NIGHT BETWEEN
LETTER-OF-INTENT SIGNING DAY AND THE START
OF SPRING FOOTBALL...

# HUSKERNUTZ

FOR SOME OF US, TAILGATING IS AS CLOSE AS WE'LL EVER GET TO SEATS IN MEMORIAL STADIUM.

# HUSKERNUTZ

# HUSKERNUTZ

YOU CAN ALWAYS SPOT THE FANS WHO DROVE ALL NIGHT FROM THE OTHER END OF THE STATE TO BE THERE FOR HUSKER KICKOFF.

# HUSKERNUTZ

SOMETIMES YOU CAN SPOT A BUDDING HUSKER
SUPERSTAR IN THE EARLY STAGES OF DEVELOPMENT.

# HUSKERNUTZ

DELBERT CLAPPER COMES UP WITH WHAT HE
THINKS IS THE BUSINESS IDEA OF THE CENTURY.

# HUSKERNUTZ

LORETTA RECORDS HER LIFE'S MILESTONES...
WEDDING ANNIVERSARIES... KIDS' BIRTHDAYS...
LETTER OF INTENT SIGNING DAY... SPRING FOOTBALL...
FALL PRACTICE... SEASON OPENER.

# HUSKERNUTZ

BLINDED BY HIS LOVE OF ALL THINGS HUSKER, LAMONT PUSHES THE "CASUAL FRIDAY" DRESS CODE TOO FAR.

# HUSKERNUTZ

YOU NEVER TIRE OF BRAGGING ABOUT YOUR
AMAZING ONE-HANDED CATCH... OF A HOT DOG SHOT
FROM DER WEINERSCHLINGER.

# HUSKERNUTZ

GEORGE AND LILLIAN CHALLENGE THE "NO FANS ON THE MEMORIAL STADIUM PLAYING SURFACE" POLICY.

# HUSKERNUTZ

WHILE WE REALLY DON'T BELIEVE IN SANTA, IT DOESN'T HURT TO HAVE ALL THE BASES COVERED.

# HUSKERNUTZ

HUSKER FANS ARE THE EASIEST PEOPLE IN THE
WORLD TO SHOP FOR AT CHRISTMAS TIME.

# HUSKERNUTZ

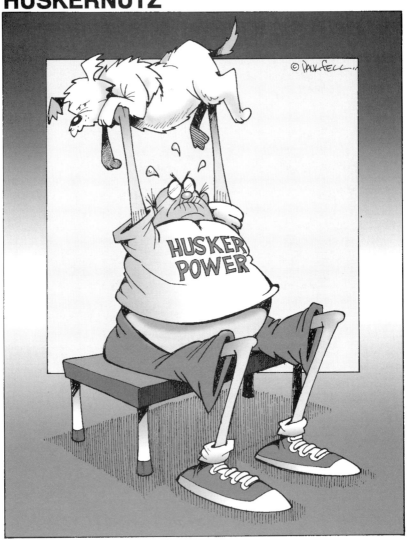

BUSTER HOPES THE TEAM'S WINTER CONDITIONING
PROGRAM IS GOING AS WELL AS HIS HOME VERSION.

# HUSKERNUTZ

BUCK AND NATALIE'S DIVORCE WAS PROCEEDING
SMOOTHLY UNTIL THE ISSUE OF N.U. SEASON
TICKETS SURFACED.

# HUSKERNUTZ

HUSKER KIDS HAVE A PERFECT EXCUSE WHEN
THEY'RE LATE FOR DINNER.

# HUSKERNUTZ

OCCASIONALLY, SOME OF US START THINKING OF
OUR **DAUGHTER'S** CAREER AS A HUSKER.

# HUSKERNUTZ

NEXT TIME YOU ARE TEMPTED TO COMPLAIN ABOUT
RISING GAS PRICES, TAKE A GOOD LOOK AT YOUR
HUSKER SEASON TICKETS.

# HUSKERNUTZ

JUSTIN TREASURES THAT PIECE OF GOAL POST HE
RECEIVED AS A SOUVENIR FROM A HISTORIC HUSKER
VICTORY.

# HUSKERNUTZ

HAVING JUST ONE ROOM IN THE HOUSE DEDICATED
TO THE HUSKERS IS NOT ENOUGH FOR SOME OF US.

# HUSKERNUTZ

EVEN THOUGH BUCKY'S WIFE ISN'T A BIG FAN, SHE STILL ALLOWS HIM TO HAVE HIS OWN HUSKER ROOM.

# HUSKERNUTZ

YOU HAVE TO DO AN EXTRA LOAD OF "REDS" EACH
SUNDAY DURING HUSKER FOOTBALL SEASON.

# HUSKERNUTZ

WE ALL KNOW SPRING FOOTBALL IS JUST AROUND
THE CORNER WHEN MR. FERNWACKER STARTS TO
PLAY OUT IN THE YARD WITH HIS DOG, NED.

# HUSKERNUTZ

THEY SHOULD ERECT A MONUMENT AT THE STADIUM TO HONOR THOSE HARDY SOULS WHO HAVE NEVER HAD SEASON TICKETS BUT WHO ALSO NEVER MISS A HOME GAME.

# HUSKERNUTZ

WHEN THE HUSKERS HAVE AN OPEN DATE, YOU HAVE
TO FIND A FOOTBALL GAME TO WATCH.
SOMEWHERE. ANYWHERE.

# HUSKERNUTZ

PACKING FOR A HUSKER AWAY GAME IS EASY.
JUST DUMP ALL YOUR STUFF IN A SUITCASE AND
TOSS OUT EVERYTHING THAT'S NOT RED.

# HUSKERNUTZ

SOMEHOW, BUCKY'S GREAT BUSINESS SCHEME OF
PAINTING VEHICLES FOR FOOTBALL SEASON NEVER
SEEMED TO CATCH ON.

# HUSKERNUTZ

YOU COMPLAIN ABOUT PAYING A QUARTER TO PARK DOWNTOWN DURING THE WEEK, BUT THINK NOTHING OF HANDING OVER $500 FOR A PRIME GAME DAY TAILGATE LOCATION.

# HUSKERNUTZ

YOU NEVER SEEM TO BAG MANY PHEASANTS WHEN
THE HUSKER GAME IS ON THE RADIO.

# HUSKERNUTZ

YOU CAN REMEMBER WHEN IF A KID SAID HE
WANTED TO PITCH FOR THE HUSKERS, IT MEANT
HE WANTED TO PLAY QUARTERBACK.

# HUSKERNUTZ

SERIOUS HUSKERS THINK AN APPROPRIATE BABY
GIFT IS A RATTLE SHAPED LIKE A SET OF BARBELLS.

# HUSKERNUTZ

ONE OF THE GREAT MYSTERIES OF MEMORIAL STADIUM IS HOW THEY MANAGE TO GET ALL THOSE 36" REAR ENDS INTO THOSE 18" SEATS.

# HUSKERNUTZ

HOWIE HAS DISCOVERED A WAY TO MAKE HIS HUSKER
FOOTBALL WEEKENDS PAY FOR THEMSELVES.

# HUSKERNUTZ

YOU'D LOVE SANTA EVEN IF HE DIDN'T WEAR RED,
BUT PROBABLY NOT NEARLY AS MUCH.

# HUSKERNUTZ

YOUR WIFE REFUSES TO LET YOU TAKE THE KIDS
SHOPPING FOR SCHOOL CLOTHES.

# HUSKERNUTZ

YOU ARE SUCH A BIG HUSKER FAN THAT YOUR SON
BRINGS YOU TO SCHOOL FOR SHOW AND TELL.

# HUSKERNUTZ

AS THE START OF THE SEASON APPROACHES, YOUR
SUPERSTITIONS GET OUT OF HAND.

# HUSKERNUTZ

YOU ALWAYS ALLOW PLENTY OF TIME FOR TAILGATING
BEFORE THE GAME.

# HUSKERNUTZ

TECHNOLOGY BRINGS MORE HUSKER FANS THAN
EVER TO MEMORIAL STADIUM.

# HUSKERNUTZ

HUSKER FANS LOOK FORWARD TO BISON STEAKS FOR
THANKSGIVING, AND PRAY THEY DON'T HAVE TO SETTLE
FOR EATING CROW.

# HUSKERNUTZ

YOUR BROTHER LETS YOU USE HIS TICKETS IN THE
UPPER DECK OF THE EAST STADIUM.
THEY PROVE TO BE FARTHER AWAY FROM THE FIELD
THAN YOU THOUGHT.

# HUSKERNUTZ

YOU LOVE VALENTINE'S DAY BECAUSE YOU GET TO
WEAR ALL THAT NEAT STUFF YOU'VE HAD IN STORAGE
SINCE THE COLORADO GAME.

# HUSKERNUTZ

AFTER A LONG, HARD DAY YOU ENJOY COMING
HOME TO THAT SPECIAL PLACE TO RELAX, REFLECT,
AND REGROUP.

# HUSKERNUTZ

MARION WILL BE HAPPIER THAN MEL WHEN HUSKER FOOTBALL SEASON FINALLY GETS UNDERWAY.

# HUSKERNUTZ

VELDA IS STARTING TO REGRET HAVING TRAINED
ROCKY TO ENJOY WATCHING NEBRASKA GAMES
ON TELEVISION.

# HUSKERNUTZ

IT'S HARD TO BELIEVE THAT JUST A COUPLE OF YEARS AGO THE MAIN SPRING SPORT IN THESE PARTS WAS YOU-KNOW-WHAT.

# HUSKERNUTZ

DOCTORS NOTICE AN UNUSUAL NUMBER OF HIGH
BLOOD PRESSURE COMPLAINTS RIGHT AFTER
THE HUSKERS WIN A CLOSE GAME.

# HUSKERNUTZ

YOU WILL GO CHRISTMAS SHOPPING WITH YOUR SPOUSE... BUT ONLY UNDER CERTAIN CONDITIONS.

# HUSKERNUTZ

SOME HUSKER FANS ARE GETTING SO SPOILED THAT THEY'RE NOT SATSIFIED WITH JUST ANY OLD VICTORY.

# HUSKERNUTZ

WHEN YOU CAN'T GET TICKETS AND HAVE TO
WATCH THE GAME ON TV, YOU TRY TO REPLICATE
STADIUM CONDITIONS AS CLOSELY AS YOU CAN.

# HUSKERNUTZ

YOU OWN SEVERAL TELEVISION SETS IN CASE
ONE BREAKS DOWN DURING LIVE COVERAGE
OF A HUSKER GAME.

# HUSKERNUTZ

YOU CAN REMEMBER WHEN YOU SHOOK HANDS
WITH THE LEGENDARY BOB DEVANEY.

# HUSKERNUTZ

YOU'RE OLD ENOUGH TO REMEMBER A TIME
WHEN THE HUSKERS **DIDN'T** GO TO
A BOWL GAME EVERY YEAR.

# HUSKERNUTZ

YOUR FAMILY KNOWS BETTER THAN TO BOTHER
YOU WITH PETTY ISSUES ON HUSKER GAME DAYS.

# HUSKERNUTZ

FOR SOME OF US, THE HARDEST TIME OF THE YEAR IS THE PERIOD BETWEEN THE BOWL GAME AND NATIONAL LETTER OF INTENT SIGNING DAY.

# HUSKERNUTZ

YOU CAN NEVER REMEMBER WHERE YOU LEFT YOUR CAR KEYS OR GLASSES, BUT YOU KNOW WHO THE HUSKERS WILL BE PLAYING FOR THE NEXT 5 YEARS.

# HUSKERNUTZ

HUSKERNUTS TAKE THOSE RARE LOSSES A LOT
HARDER THAN THE AVERAGE FAN DOES.

# HUSKERNUTZ

YOU'RE OLD ENOUGH TO REMEMBER WHEN THINGS
WERE A LOT SIMPLER. NOT BETTER... JUST SIMPLER.

# HUSKERNUTZ

YOUR UNCLE'S WILL STIPULATES THAT YOU GET HIS SEASON TICKETS, BUT ONLY UNDER CERTAIN CONDITIONS.

# HUSKERNUTZ

THE FIRST THING YOU DO AFTER YOUR SEASON
TICKETS ARRIVE IN THE MAIL IS TO GO DOWN AND
SIGN UP FOR A BOWL GAME TOUR.

# HUSKERNUTZ

YOU ARE INSULTED WHEN YOU OFFER YOUR
GAME TICKETS TO SOMEONE AND HE WANTS
TO KNOW WHERE YOUR SEATS ARE LOCATED
BEFORE HE ACCEPTS.

# HUSKERNUTZ

MOST PEOPLE KNOW BETTER THAN TO PAY
SOCIAL CALLS AT YOUR HOUSE ON GAME DAY.

# HUSKERNUTZ

YOU CAN'T IMAGINE WHY ANYONE WOULD LEAVE
A HUSKER GAME BEFORE THE FINAL GUN.

# HUSKERNUTZ

HUSKERNUTZ LIVE IN A CONSTANT STATE OF
ANXIOUS ANTICIPATION.

# HUSKERNUTZ

IF YOU CAN'T BE AT THE STADIUM ON GAME DAY,
YOU MAKE SURE YOU DON'T MISS ANY OF
THE ACTION.

# HUSKERNUTZ

YOU ARE BANNED FOR LIFE FROM SCOTTSBLUFF
NATIONAL MONUMENT FOR TRYING TO CARVE THE
FACES OF DEVANEY, OSBORNE AND SOLICH,
A LA MOUNT RUSHMORE.

# HUSKERNUTZ

WITH FOOTBALL SEASON OVER, LIFE RETURNS
TO NORMAL FOR MOST HUSKER FANS.

# HUSKERNUTZ

FOR SOME OF US, THE DARK AGES IS THE TIME
BETWEEN THE HUSKER BOWL GAME AND THE
START OF SPRING PRACTICE.

# HUSKERNUTZ

TELEMARKETERS SHOULD KNOW BETTER THAN
TO CALL ANYWHERE IN NEBRASKA WHEN THE
HUSKERS ARE PLAYING.

# HUSKERNUTZ

30 YEARS AGO YOU USED TO SCALE THE SOUTH
STADIUM FENCE TO GET INTO HUSKER GAMES.
NOW IT'S TOUGH JUST SQUEEZING THROUGH
THE TURNSTILES.

# HUSKERNUTZ

YOU KNEW YOUR BRIDE WAS AN OKAY GAL WHEN
SHE LET YOU PICK OUT THE TUXEDOS FOR YOUR
WEDDING.

# HUSKERNUTZ

NEBRASKA FANS WILL BUY ANYTHING THAT'S
FOR SALE AT HUSKER HOME GAMES.